THE CLONE WARS

THE STARCRUSHER TRAP

DESIGNER **AIMEE DANIELSON-GERMANY**

ASSISTANT EDITOR **FREDDYE LINS**

EDITOR **RANDY STRADLEY**

PUBLISHER **MIKE RICHARDSON**

Special thanks to Jann Moorhead, David Anderman, Troy Alders, Leland Chee, Sue Rostoni, and Carol Roeder at Lucas Licensing.

Published by Dark Horse Books, a division of Dark Horse Comics, Inc.
10956 SE Main Street, Milwaukie, OR 97222

DarkHorse.com | StarWars.com

To find a comics shop in your area, call the Comic Shop Locator Service toll-free at 1.888.266.4226
Scholastic edition: July 2011 | ISBN 978-1-59582-831-6

PRINTED AT SOLISCO PRINTERS, LTD., SCOTT, QC, CANADA

STAR WARS®

THE CLONE WARS™

THE STARCRUSHER TRAP

SCRIPT **MIKE W. BARR**   ART **THE FILLBACH BROTHERS**

COLORS **RAYMUND LEE**   LETTERING **MICHAEL HEISLER**

COVER ART **THE FILLBACH BROTHERS WITH DAN JACKSON**

DARK HORSE BOOKS®

THE RISE OF THE EMPIRE
1000–0 YEARS BEFORE *STAR WARS: A NEW HOPE*

The events in these stories take place approximately twenty-two years before the Battle of Yavin.

After the seeming final defeat of the Sith, the Republic enters a state of complacency. In the waning years of the Republic, the Senate is rife with corruption, and the ambitious Senator Palpatine has himself elected Supreme Chancellor. This is the era of the prequel trilogy.

ON AN ASTEROID DEEP INSIDE ENEMY SPACE SITS A MUNITIONS FACTORY, PRODUCING WEAPONS OF WAR FOR THE SEPARATIST MOVEMENT.

PROTECTED AGAINST ALL ASSAULTS BY A FORCE FIELD, THE FACTORY HAS PROVEN TO BE INVULNERABLE TO ALL STARSHIP ATTACKS.

BUT TWO JEDI KNIGHTS MAY BE MORE FORMIDABLE THAN A FLEET OF STARSHIPS.

MASTER KENOBI, I THINK I FORGOT THE EXPLOSIVES!

WHAT?

THOOM!

HEY! MY STABILIZERS--!

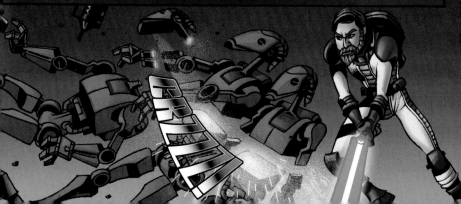

BRZZZ

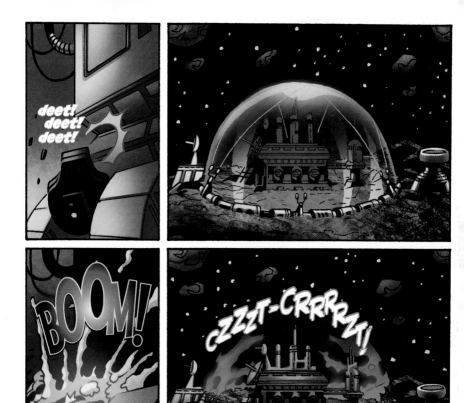

SHIELDS *RAISED,* SIR!

PREPARE FOR --

WHOOOOM!

ALL THREE SHIPS DESTROYED, ADMIRAL KIRST.

GOOD.

WIDE-ANGLE SPREAD. TARGET ANY ESCAPE PODS AND FIRE.

SHOULDN'T THE TASK FORCE HAVE ATTACKED BY NOW?

I WOULD HAVE THOUGHT SO. HAVE YOU CALLED FOR OUR EXTRACTION?

ON IT NOW, MASTER.

WHERE'D ALL THIS *WRECKAGE* COME FROM?

I'M AFRAID I *KNOW*, JYL...

...AND I THINK *THAT'S* THE REASON!

WOW...!

WELL, ARE YOU JUST GOING TO FLY *INTO* IT?

IT'S TOO LATE TO *AVOID* IT, MASTER...

≥WHEW≤

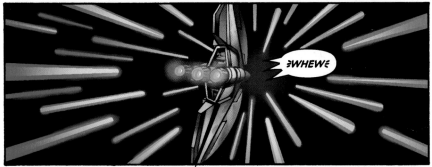

THE TRANSPORT ELUDED US, ADMIRAL.

JUST AS WELL. THE MORE *EYEWITNESSES* TO OUR VICTORY, THE QUICKER *FEAR* OF THE *STARCRUSHER* WILL SPREAD THROUGH THE REPUBLIC!

VERY WELL, COUNT DOOKU. I SHALL BE IN TOUCH.

...AND THOUGH THE STARCRUSHER PERFORMED ADMIRABLY, LORD SIDIOUS, HAD THE JEDI BEEN ANY EARLIER, THE FACTORY WOULD HAVE BEEN DESTROYED.

THE JEDI. ALWAYS THE CURSED JEDI. IF HIS PLAN IS TO ACHIEVE FRUITION, THEY MUST BE ELIMINATED.

BUT HOW...?

THE SCOWL OF DARTH SIDIOUS IS THOUGHT TO BE A FEARSOME SIGHT...

OF COURSE.

...UNTIL ONE SEES HIS SMILE.

...AND I THINK I ALREADY KNOW *WHO.* AHSOKA, WE HAVE A *MISSION.*

YES, MASTER KENOBI. YOU, MASTER SKYWALKER, AND ME?

NOT QUITE, SNIPS...

...I WON'T BE WITH YOU ON THIS ONE. BUT I'M SURE YOU'LL DO FINE.

YES, MASTER, BUT...WHERE *WILL* YOU BE?

ANAKIN'S PLAYING *ERRAND BOY* FOR THE CHANCELLOR AGAIN. NICE TO BE TEACHER'S PET, *EH?*

JEALOUS? CHANCELLOR PALPATINE KNOWS THE *BEST* WHEN HE SEES IT, JYL.

STOP IT...!

CHANCELLOR PALPATINE, HOW MAY THE JEDI BE OF SERVICE?

AH, ANAKIN! YOU MAY BE OF SERVICE TO THE REPUBLIC...

...BY DELIVERING THESE SEEDS TO THE GOVERNMENT OF *DALTARRI.* AS PLANT-BASED BEINGS, THEY WILL SEE THIS AS A SIGN OF *GOODWILL.*

THAT'S *IT?* JUST DELIVER SOME *SEEDS?*

PATIENCE, ANAKIN! ONE NEVER KNOWS HOW LONG IT WILL TAKE A SEED TO *BEAR FRUIT!*

28

"...AND I THINK OUR PLAN WORKED! OUR ASSAULT SUMMONED THE *STARCRUSHER*...

"...THEY'RE DEPLOYING A SHUTTLE. *HMM,* I'M NOT READING ANY LIFE FORMS."

THIS MAY BE OUR ONLY CHANCE! YOU HAVE YOUR ORDERS!

YES, MASTER! OUR SHUTTLE HAS BEEN PROGRAMMED AS YOU DIRECTED!

30

"--I READ A *SHUTTLE* PULLING AWAY FROM THE *AFT AIRLOCK,* SIR!"

WHAT--?

IT SEEMS YOU SPOKE *TOO SOON,* CAPTAIN! LET MY DROIDS BOARD YOUR LITTLE SHIP TO SWEEP FOR *INTRUDERS--*

--AND WE'LL TAKE CARE OF THAT TROUBLESOME *SHUTTLE,* TOO!

CROOM!

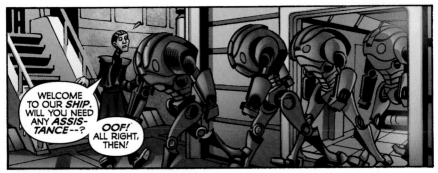

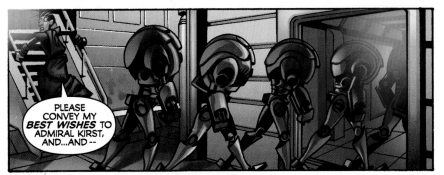

PLEASE CONVEY MY *BEST WISHES* TO ADMIRAL KIRST, AND...AND --

MY, *THEY* WERE CERTAINLY RUDE! PREPARE TO LEAVE THE SYSTEM!

THE DROIDS ARE RETURNING, ADMIRAL KIRST. THEIR DOWNLOAD READS NO REPORT WITH HOSTILES.

I *KNEW* IT! WHATEVER THE REPUBLIC WAS ATTEMPTING, IT *DIED* WITH THEIR SHUTTLE!

ALL RIGHT, YOU DROIDS, YOU HAVE YOUR ORDERS! STRAIGHT TO *MAINTENANCE*, AND THEN--

KRNNG!

OWWW--!

JUST IN *TIME!* I MIGHT NOT HAVE BEEN ABLE TO STAY HIDDEN THERE FOR MUCH LONGER!

AHSOKA--YOU, MASTER SOMTAY, AND I WILL SABOTAGE THE *LIFE-SUPPORT* SYSTEMS! OBI-WAN AND KI-ADI-MUNDI SHALL DISABLE THE *WEAPONS ARRAY!*

"...ABANDON SHIP!"

FWOOOOSHT!

SURRENDER, AND THERE WILL BE NO--

WHAT--?

STAND DOWN! DROP ALL WEAPONS, OR--

MASTER *KI..!*

THIS IS CERTAINLY ODD.

...THERE IS NO *CREW.*

CURIOUS.

MASTER KI --

--THE SHIP SEEMS *DESERTED.* BUT HOW CAN THAT BE?

SOME *ESCAPE PODS* WERE LAUNCHED...BUT NOT NEARLY ENOUGH TO ACCOUNT FOR THE *ENTIRE CREW...*

"BACK TO THE *HANGAR BAY*-- IMMEDIATELY."

WHAT'S THIS *ABOUT*, MASTERS?

I FEEL A DISTURBANCE IN THE FORCE! THIS IS *NOT* RIGHT!

THE HANGAR BAY IS RIGHT AHEAD --

IS EVERYONE *ALL RIGHT?*

I BELIEVE *SO,* MASTER --

I FEAR WE HAVE BEEN *FOOLS,* MORE EASILY DECEIVED THAN THE MOST NAIVE *YOUNGLING...*

...THESE MECHANISMS ARE *HOLLOW* -- THEY ARE ONLY *SHELLS!*

LOOK AT *THIS,* MASTERS...

...THIS *CONSOLE* IS *EMPTY* -- JUST A *BOX* WITH SOME FLASHING LIGHTS. THEY *ALL* ARE.

AND SO --

40

THE SITUATION IS AS BAD AS WE **SUSPECTED.** THIS **"SHIP"** IS **HOLLOW,** WITH LITTLE **POWER** AND NO **NAVIGATIONAL CAPABILITY.**

THAT **LURCH** WE FELT WAS MOST OF ITS REMAINING POWER BEING EXPENDED AS IT SHIFTED **COURSE.**

EVEN THE **LIFE-SUPPORT** SYSTEM IS A FACSIMILE, **USELESS.**

WE HAVE AIR TO BREATHE, BUT WITHOUT THE OTHER SYSTEMS, EVENTUALLY THE SHIP WILL GROW **COLD.**

COLD, MASTER KI?

I DON'T THINK **COLD** WILL BE A PROBLEM!

WE SHOULD BE *FLATTERED,* ACTUALLY...THAT THEY WENT TO ALL THIS TROUBLE TO GET RID OF *US.*

BUT *BURNING* TO DEATH...THAT'LL BE BAD. FREEZING WOULD BE BETTER. AT LEAST YOU'D BE *NUMB...*

THAT'S *ENOUGH,* MASTER SOMTAY! REMEMBER YOUR *TRAINING!* WE ARE *JEDI!* WE DO NOT *SUCCUMB* TO *DESPAIR!*

WE *WILL* ESCAPE THIS! IS THAT *CLEAR?*

Y-YES, MASTER WINDU...BUT *HOW?*

I DON'T *KNOW* YET.

TELL THE CHANCELLOR THAT WE DALTARRI VALUE ABOVE ALL ELSE OUR *ALLIES...* THOSE WHO WILL AID YOU WITHOUT *QUESTION.*

WE, TOO, APPRECIATE OUR ALLIES, AND --

PLEASE *PARDON* ME, YOUR GRACE --

-- I HATE TO CUT OUR VISIT *SHORT*, BUT I MUST *DEPART...* ON URGENT BUSINESS.

UNDERSTOOD, MASTER SKYWALKER. MAY YOU HAVE SUNLIGHT, ABUNDANT WATER, AND DEEP *ROOTS.*

FIRE UP THE *ENGINES,* ARTOO-DETOO -- WE'RE *LEAVING.*

VADA BLOOT? WHEET?

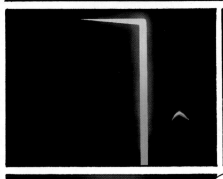

49

51

52

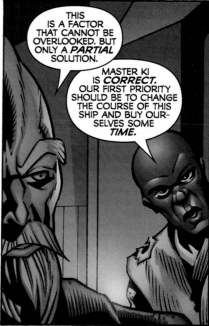

54

IF YOU'RE IN A HUGE HULK OF A STARSHIP THAT'S DRIFTING TOWARD THIS SYSTEM'S *SUN* --

-- I THINK I'M RIGHT *OUTSIDE!*

I'VE DEFIED THE CHANCELLOR'S *ORDERS.* IT'S THAT *REBELLIOUS STREAK* OF MINE YOU KEEP *CAUTIONING* ME ABOUT, I'M *AFRAID!*

BLESS THAT REBELLIOUS STREAK! FOR ONCE, YOU'RE RIGHT WHERE I *WANT* YOU!

WE'RE ON THE *BRIDGE,* ANAKIN. WE CAN *SEE* YOU! HERE'S WHAT WE NEED YOU TO *DO* --

UH-OH...!

THE *REAL* STARCRUSHER HAS ARRIVED, ADMIRAL.

EXCELLENT. OUR PLAN NEARS FRUITION! PUT ME THROUGH TO THE SHIP!

GET US ABOARD *QUICKLY,* CAPTAIN!

YES, ADMIRAL!

I'D BETTER MAKE MYSELF SCARCE BEFORE THEY *SEE* ME!

NO, ANAKIN! OUR ONLY CHANCE IS FOR YOU TO *BOARD* THAT SHIP BEFORE YOUR PRESENCE IS DETECTED! CAN YOU DO THAT?

62

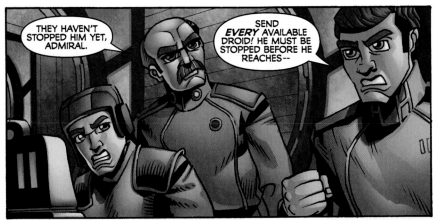

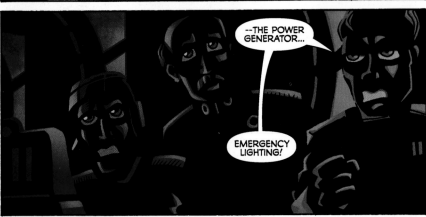

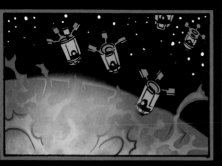

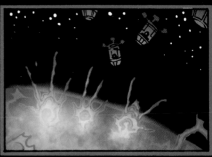

THERE THEY *GO...*

AND WE'RE *NEXT!*

WE HAVEN'T GIVEN UP *YET!*

GET READY...

LIEUTENANT DAAN, I HOPE YOU DISCONNECTED THE *MAGNETIC COIL* -- OR THIS WILL BE A VERY *SHORT* TRIP!

AS YOU *ORDERED,* MASTER KENOBI! BUT--

IS THAT *TETHER* GOOD AND TIGHT? THEN HERE WE *GO...*

73

THIS IS EVEN WORSE THAN FLYING!

MASTER WINDU--?

YES, MASTER SOMTAY?

I JUST WANTED TO *APOLOGIZE* FOR MY FEARS ABOARD THE *STARCRUSHER*--

FEAR IS AN *EMOTION,* MASTER SOMTAY. BE MINDFUL OF YOUR FEELINGS, BUT NEVER LET THEM CONTROL YOUR ACTIONS.

YES, MASTER. *THANK* YOU.

HEY, SKYGUY! HOW'D IT GO WITH THE *CHANCELLOR?*

BETTER THAN I *THOUGHT.* HE DIDN'T SEEM MAD AT ALL AT ME FOR SKIPPING OUT ON HIS MISSION.

SO WHAT ARE YOU TWO UP TO?

GOING OUT FOR A CAF AND A LITTLE *GIRL TALK.*

OH? ABOUT WHAT?

THE END

STAR WARS GRAPHIC NOVEL TIMELINE (IN YEARS)

Omnibus: Tales of the Jedi—5,000–3,986 BSW4
Knights of the Old Republic—3,964–3,963 BSW4
The Old Republic—3653, 3678 BSW4
Knight Errant—1,032 BSW4
Jedi vs. Sith—1,000 BSW4
Omnibus: Rise of the Sith—33 BSW4
Episode I: The Phantom Menace—32 BSW4
Omnibus: Emissaries and Assassins—32 BSW4
Twilight—31 BSW4
Omnibus: Menace Revealed—31–22 BSW4
Darkness—30 BSW4
The Stark Hyperspace War—30 BSW4
Rite of Passage—28 BSW4
Honor and Duty—22 BSW4
Blood Ties—22 BSW4
Episode II: Attack of the Clones—22 BSW4
Clone Wars—22–19 BSW4
Clone Wars Adventures—22–19 BSW4
General Grievous—22–19 BSW4
Episode III: Revenge of the Sith—19 BSW4
Dark Times—19 BSW4
Omnibus: Droids—5.5 BSW4
Boba Fett: Enemy of the Empire—3 BSW4
Underworld—1 BSW4
Episode IV: A New Hope—SW4
Classic Star Wars—0–3 ASW4
A Long Time Ago . . . —0–4 ASW4
Empire—0 ASW4
Rebellion—0 ASW4
Boba Fett: Man with a Mission—0 ASW4
Omnibus: Early Victories—0–3 ASW4
Jabba the Hutt: The Art of the Deal—1 ASW4
Episode V: The Empire Strikes Back—3 ASW4
Omnibus: Shadows of the Empire—3.5–4.5 ASW4
Episode VI: Return of the Jedi—4 ASW4
Omnibus: X-Wing Rogue Squadron—4–5 ASW4
Heir to the Empire—9 ASW4
Dark Force Rising—9 ASW4
The Last Command—9 ASW4
Dark Empire—10 ASW4
Boba Fett: Death, Lies, and Treachery—10 ASW4
Crimson Empire—11 ASW4
Jedi Academy: Leviathan—12 ASW4
Union—19 ASW4
Chewbacca—25 ASW4
Invasion—25 ASW4
Legacy—130–137 ASW4

Old Republic Era
25,000 – 1000 years before
Star Wars: A New Hope

Rise of the Empire Era
1000 – 0 years before
Star Wars: A New Hope

Rebellion Era
0 – 5 years after
Star Wars: A New Hope

New Republic Era
5 – 25 years after
Star Wars: A New Hope

New Jedi Order Era
25+ years after
Star Wars: A New Hope

Legacy Era
130+ years after
Star Wars: A New Hope

Vector
Crosses four eras in the timeline

Volume 1
Knights of the Old Republic Volume 5
Dark Times Volume 3
Volume 2
Rebellion Volume 4
Legacy Volume 6

BSW4 = before *Episode IV: A New Hope.* ASW4 = after *Episode IV: A New Hope.*

FOR MORE ADVENTURE IN A GALAXY FAR, FAR, AWAY...